BATTLE PLAN

PRAYER JOURNAL

PRAYER WARRIOR

THE POWER OF PRAYER

There is nothing more effective that any believer can do in any circumstance than pray. Meditate on that for just a moment. We have been given the incredible privilege to come boldly before the maker of all things, our God, and speak directly to Him, asking Him to move on our behalf. Many times when things begin to go wrong in our lives, we try our best to fix them with our natural wisdom. When all else fails.... Pray. I say let prayer be your <u>first</u> response! Even if the Lord chooses to use you in some natural way, allow Him to give you His wisdom. Never let God be your last resort.

Prayer changes things is a popular saying but it is also a powerful truth! We have been given promises and covenants in the Word of God that we can take hold of by faith. The Lord tells us to believe that He loves us and will help us. He tells us that He withholds no good things from us. (Psalm 84:11) The Lord tells us that He has good plans for us, not evil ones! (Jeremiah 29:11) The Lord tells us that if we ask anything according to His will, He will give it to us! (1 John 5:14) If we had no other promise from God, that one would be enough. How do we know and pray Gods will so that our prayers are answered? God's will is revealed in His Word. God has given us many scriptures that tell us exactly what His will is. His nature and His character are revealed in the Word so we know our God and we know what He desires for us and from us.

You can actually find scriptures that can be applied to your life and circumstances and pray those scriptures. Praying and speaking the Word in this way is a powerful prayer. Whether the situation you face is salvation, healing, finances, relationships, family or any other need, there are scriptures that cover those needs. When you see in the Word that God wants all to be saved, or God desires for us to walk in perfect health or abundance, it removes doubt and allows us to pray and speak to Him in faith. Faith in Him. Faith that He is Good (Psalm 46:1) Faith that He loves us. (John 3:16) Faith that He has paid the price for our salvation in full. (Isaiah chapter 53)

When we truly get the revelation of who God is and how much He loves us it changes everything. When we look at our own children or loved ones and we are aware of how much we care for them and that we would do everything in our power to help them we can realize that God feels that way even more. The Bible says...

If you, then, though you are evil, know how to give good gifts to your children, how much more will your Father in heaven give good gifts to those who ask him!
Matthew 7:11

Ask Him!

PRAYER JOURNAL INDEX

Our Position in Christ   i

1 _____ Pg._____

2 _____ Pg._____

3 _____ Pg_____

4 _____ Pg_____

5 _____ Pg_____

6 _____ Pg_____

7 _____ Pg_____

8 _____ Pg_____

9 _____ Pg_____

10 _____ Pg_____

11 _____ Pg_____

12 _____ Pg_____

13 _____ Pg_____

14 _____ Pg_____

15 _____ Pg_____

OUR POSITION IN CHRIST

...The Lord is with you, you valiant warrior! (Judges 6:12)

I have given you authority to trample on snakes and scorpions and to overcome all the power of the enemy; nothing will harm you. (Luke 10:19)

Once you realize, or begin to realize who you are, you will begin to use the authority given to you in the Word in greater measure. This authority or position **in Christ** (Ephesians 2:6) crosses all boundaries into every area of your life. Whether at home or work, in your relationships, family and friends or ministry, you can exercise or exert the authority given you to effect all areas to see **God's will** done.

When we accept Christ as Savior and Lord, we become a different person or a different being. Something supernatural happens and we literally becomes a new creation. In addition, we inherit a position **in Christ** of authority in the realm of the Kingdom of God. You are no longer human beings as such but something far, far greater.

... Are you not acting like mere humans? (1 Corinthians 3:3)

Therefore if any man be in Christ, he is a new creature... (2 Corinthians 5:17)

Who Are You?

Who are you and what is your testimony? To engage in warfare effectively you must *know* who you are. If you are born again a part of your testimony is the following...

You are a son (daughter) of God

Beloved, now are we the sons of God, and it doth not yet appear what we shall be: but we know that when He shall appear, we shall be like Him; for we shall see Him as He is. (1 John 3:2)

You are a member of God's own household.

Consequently, you are no longer foreigners and strangers, but fellow citizens with God's people and also members of His household. (Ephesians 2:19)

You are heirs of God

And if children, then heirs; heirs of God and joint heirs with Christ; if so be that we suffer with Him, so that we may be also glorified together. (Romans 8:17)

You are loved of God and Chosen by Him

For we know, brothers and sisters loved by God, that He has chosen you. (1 Thessalonians 1:4)

You are a citizen of Heaven

But we are citizens of Heaven, where the Lord Jesus Christ lives. And we are eagerly waiting for Him to return as our Savior. (Philippians 3:20)

You are seated in Heavenly places

And God raised us up with Christ and seated us with Him in the heavenly realms in Christ Jesus. (Ephesians 2:6)

You have been given authority

Behold, I have given you authority to tread on serpents and scorpions, and over all the power of the enemy, and nothing shall hurt you. (Luke 10:19)

He has given His angels charge over you

If you say, "The Lord is my refuge," and you make the Most High your dwelling, no harm will overtake you, no disaster will come near your tent. For He will command His angels concerning you, to guard you in all your ways; They will lift you up in their hands, so that you will not strike your foot against a stone. (Psalm 91: 9 – 12)

As you place yourself "in the gap" for those you love or for those you are called to pray for, remember always that God is for you. He will accomplish great things with you and through you as you yield yourself to Him. Now just be the warrior that you are.

Be Still and Know That I Am God.
Psalm 46:10

NAME_____ DATE_____

Prayer Need or Concern

**Standing on
Scriptures**

Praise Reports / Testimonies

Notes_____

Photo

NAME_____ DATE_____

Prayer Need or Concern

Standing on Scriptures

_____   _____

_____   _____

_____   _____

_____   _____

_____   _____

_____   _____

_____   _____

Praise Reports / Testimonies

_____

_____

_____

_____

_____

Notes_____

Photo

_____

_____

_____

_____

_____

_____

_____

NAME_____ DATE_____

Prayer Need or Concern

Standing on Scriptures

_____ _____
_____ _____
_____ _____
_____ _____
_____ _____
_____ _____
_____ _____
_____

Praise Reports / Testimonies

_____
_____
_____
_____
_____

Notes_____ **Photo**

_____
_____
_____
_____
_____
_____
_____
_____
_____

NAME_____ DATE_____

Prayer Need or Concern

Standing on Scriptures

Praise Reports / Testimonies

Notes_____

Photo

NAME_____ DATE_____

Prayer Need or Concern

Standing on Scriptures

Praise Reports / Testimonies

Notes_____

Photo

NAME_____ DATE_____

Prayer Need or Concern

Standing on Scriptures

Praise Reports / Testimonies

Notes_____

Photo

NAME_____ DATE_____

Prayer Need or Concern

Standing on Scriptures

Praise Reports / Testimonies

Notes_____

Photo

NAME_____ DATE_____

Prayer Need or Concern

Standing on Scriptures

Praise Reports / Testimonies

Notes_____

Photo

NAME_____ DATE_____

Prayer Need or Concern

Standing on Scriptures

_____   _____
_____   _____
_____   _____
_____   _____
_____   _____
_____   _____
_____   _____

Praise Reports / Testimonies

_____
_____
_____
_____
_____

Notes_____

Photo

_____
_____
_____
_____
_____
_____
_____
_____

NAME_____ DATE_____

Prayer Need or Concern

Standing on Scriptures

Praise Reports / Testimonies

Notes_____

Photo

NAME_____ DATE_____

Prayer Need or Concern

Standing on Scriptures

Praise Reports / Testimonies

Notes

Photo

NAME_____ DATE_____

Prayer Need or Concern

Standing on Scriptures

_____   _____
_____   _____
_____   _____
_____   _____
_____   _____
_____   _____
_____   _____
_____   _____

Praise Reports / Testimonies

_____
_____
_____
_____
_____

Notes_____

_____
_____
_____
_____
_____
_____
_____
_____

Photo

NAME_____ DATE_____

Prayer Need or Concern

**Standing on
Scriptures**

_____   _____
_____   _____
_____   _____
_____   _____
_____   _____
_____   _____
_____   _____
_____   _____

Praise Reports / Testimonies

_____
_____
_____
_____
_____

Notes_____   **Photo**

_____
_____
_____
_____
_____
_____
_____

NAME_____ DATE_____

Prayer Need or Concern

Standing on Scriptures

_____   _____
_____   _____
_____   _____
_____   _____
_____   _____
_____   _____
_____   _____

Praise Reports / Testimonies

_____
_____
_____
_____
_____

Notes_____

Photo

_____
_____
_____
_____
_____
_____
_____
_____

NAME_____ DATE_____

Prayer Need or Concern

Standing on Scriptures

_____   _____
_____   _____
_____   _____
_____   _____
_____   _____
_____   _____
_____   _____
_____   _____

Praise Reports / Testimonies

_____
_____
_____
_____

Notes_____   **Photo**

_____
_____
_____
_____
_____
_____
_____
_____

NAME_____ DATE_____

Prayer Need or Concern

Standing on Scriptures

_____ _____
_____ _____
_____ _____
_____ _____
_____ _____
_____ _____
_____ _____
_____

Praise Reports / Testimonies

_____
_____
_____
_____
_____

Notes_____

Photo

_____
_____
_____
_____
_____
_____
_____
_____
_____

NAME_____ DATE_____

Prayer Need or Concern

Standing on Scriptures

_____   _____
_____   _____
_____   _____
_____   _____
_____   _____
_____   _____
_____   _____
_____

Praise Reports / Testimonies

_____
_____
_____
_____
_____

Notes_____   **Photo**

_____
_____
_____
_____
_____
_____
_____
_____

NAME_____ DATE_____

Prayer Need or Concern

Standing on Scriptures

_____   _____
_____   _____
_____   _____
_____   _____
_____   _____
_____   _____
_____   _____

Praise Reports / Testimonies

_____
_____
_____
_____
_____

Notes_____   **Photo**

_____
_____
_____
_____
_____
_____
_____

NAME_____ DATE_____

Prayer Need or Concern

Standing on Scriptures

_____   _____

_____   _____

_____   _____

_____   _____

_____   _____

_____   _____

_____   _____

Praise Reports / Testimonies

_____

_____

_____

_____

_____

Notes_____   **Photo**

_____

_____

_____

_____

_____

_____

_____

_____

NAME_____ DATE_____

Prayer Need or Concern

Standing on Scriptures

_____

_____

_____

_____

_____

_____

_____

Praise Reports / Testimonies

_____

_____

_____

_____

_____

Notes_____

Photo

NAME_____ DATE_____

Prayer Need or Concern

Standing on Scriptures

Praise Reports / Testimonies

Notes_____

Photo

NAME_____ DATE_____

Prayer Need or Concern

Standing on Scriptures

Praise Reports / Testimonies

Notes_____

Photo

NAME_____ DATE_____

Prayer Need or Concern

Standing on Scriptures

_____   _____
_____   _____
_____   _____
_____   _____
_____   _____
_____   _____
_____   _____

Praise Reports / Testimonies

_____
_____
_____
_____
_____

Notes_____   **Photo**
_____
_____
_____
_____
_____
_____
_____
_____
_____

NAME_____ DATE_____

Prayer Need or Concern

Standing on Scriptures

_____   _____

_____   _____

_____   _____

_____   _____

_____   _____

_____   _____

_____   _____

Praise Reports / Testimonies

_____

_____

_____

_____

_____

Notes_____   ## Photo

_____

_____

_____

_____

_____

_____

_____

NAME_____ DATE_____

Prayer Need or Concern

Standing on Scriptures

_____   _____

_____   _____

_____   _____

_____   _____

_____   _____

_____   _____

_____   _____

Praise Reports / Testimonies

_____

_____

_____

_____

_____

Notes_____   **Photo**

_____

_____

_____

_____

_____

_____

_____

NAME_____ DATE_____

Prayer Need or Concern

Standing on Scriptures

Praise Reports / Testimonies

Notes_____

Photo

NAME_____ DATE_____

Prayer Need or Concern

Standing on Scriptures

_____   _____
_____   _____
_____   _____
_____   _____
_____   _____
_____   _____
_____   _____

Praise Reports / Testimonies

_____
_____
_____
_____

Notes _____   ## Photo

_____
_____
_____
_____
_____
_____
_____
_____

NAME_____ DATE_____

Prayer Need or Concern

Standing on Scriptures

Praise Reports / Testimonies

Notes_____

Photo

NAME_____ DATE_____

Prayer Need or Concern

Standing on Scriptures

_____   _____
_____   _____
_____   _____
_____   _____
_____   _____
_____   _____
_____   _____

Praise Reports / Testimonies

_____
_____
_____
_____
_____

Notes_____   **Photo**

_____   ┌──────────────────┐
_____   │   │
_____   │   │
_____   │   │
_____   │   │
_____   │   │
_____   │   │
_____   └──────────────────┘

NAME_____ DATE_____

Prayer Need or Concern

Standing on Scriptures

Praise Reports / Testimonies

Notes_____

Photo

NAME_____ DATE_____

Prayer Need or Concern

Standing on Scriptures

_____   _____
_____   _____
_____   _____
_____   _____
_____   _____
_____   _____
_____   _____

Praise Reports / Testimonies

_____
_____
_____
_____

Notes _____

Photo

_____
_____
_____
_____
_____
_____
_____
_____

NAME_____ DATE_____

Prayer Need or Concern

Standing on Scriptures

_____   _____
_____   _____
_____   _____
_____   _____
_____   _____
_____   _____
_____   _____

Praise Reports / Testimonies

_____
_____
_____
_____
_____
_____

Notes_____   **Photo**

_____
_____
_____
_____
_____
_____
_____
_____

NAME_____ DATE_____

Prayer Need or Concern

Standing on Scriptures

Praise Reports / Testimonies

Notes_____

Photo

NAME_____ DATE_____

Prayer Need or Concern

Standing on Scriptures

_____   _____
_____   _____
_____   _____
_____   _____
_____   _____
_____   _____
_____   _____
_____   _____

Praise Reports / Testimonies

_____
_____
_____
_____
_____

Notes_____

Photo

_____
_____
_____
_____
_____
_____
_____
_____

NAME_____ DATE_____

Prayer Need or Concern

Standing on Scriptures

_____   _____
_____   _____
_____   _____
_____   _____
_____   _____
_____   _____
_____   _____
_____

Praise Reports / Testimonies

_____
_____
_____
_____

Notes_____   ### Photo

_____
_____
_____
_____
_____
_____
_____
_____

NAME_____ DATE_____

Prayer Need or Concern

Standing on Scriptures

_____   _____
_____   _____
_____   _____
_____   _____
_____   _____
_____   _____
_____   _____

Praise Reports / Testimonies

_____
_____
_____
_____
_____

Notes_____   **Photo**

_____
_____
_____
_____
_____
_____
_____
_____

NAME_____ DATE_____

Prayer Need or Concern

Standing on Scriptures

Praise Reports / Testimonies

Notes_____

Photo

NAME_____ DATE_____

Prayer Need or Concern

Standing on Scriptures

Praise Reports / Testimonies

Notes_____

Photo

NAME_____ DATE_____

Prayer Need or Concern

Standing on Scriptures

_____   _____
_____   _____
_____   _____
_____   _____
_____   _____
_____   _____
_____   _____

Praise Reports / Testimonies

_____
_____
_____
_____
_____

Notes_____   **Photo**

_____
_____
_____
_____
_____
_____
_____
_____
_____

NAME_____ DATE_____

Prayer Need or Concern

Standing on Scriptures

_____ _____

_____ _____

_____ _____

_____ _____

_____ _____

_____ _____

_____ _____

_____ _____

Praise Reports / Testimonies

_____

_____

_____

_____

_____

Notes_____

_____

_____

_____

_____

_____

_____

_____

Photo

NAME_____ DATE_____

Prayer Need or Concern

**Standing on
Scriptures**

Praise Reports / Testimonies

Notes_____

Photo

NAME_____ DATE_____

Prayer Need or Concern

**Standing on
Scriptures**

_____   _____
_____   _____
_____   _____
_____   _____
_____   _____
_____   _____
_____   _____

Praise Reports / Testimonies

_____
_____
_____
_____
_____

Notes_____   **Photo**

_____
_____
_____
_____
_____
_____
_____
_____

NAME_____ DATE_____

Prayer Need or Concern

Standing on Scriptures

_____ _____
_____ _____
_____ _____
_____ _____
_____ _____
_____ _____
_____ _____

Praise Reports / Testimonies

_____
_____
_____
_____

Notes_____ **Photo**
_____
_____
_____
_____
_____
_____
_____
_____

NAME_____ DATE_____

Prayer Need or Concern

Standing on Scriptures

_____   _____
_____   _____
_____   _____
_____   _____
_____   _____
_____   _____
_____   _____
_____   _____

Praise Reports / Testimonies

_____
_____
_____
_____
_____

Notes_____

Photo

_____
_____
_____
_____
_____
_____
_____

NAME_____ DATE_____

Prayer Need or Concern

Standing on Scriptures

Praise Reports / Testimonies

Notes_____

Photo

NAME_____ DATE_____

Prayer Need or Concern

Standing on Scriptures

_____   _____

_____   _____

_____   _____

_____   _____

_____   _____

_____   _____

_____   _____

Praise Reports / Testimonies

_____

_____

_____

_____

_____

Notes_____

Photo

_____

_____

_____

_____

_____

_____

_____

_____

NAME_____ DATE_____

Prayer Need or Concern

Standing on Scriptures

_____

_____

_____

_____

_____

_____

_____

Praise Reports / Testimonies

_____

_____

_____

_____

_____

Notes_____

Photo

_____

_____

_____

_____

_____

_____

_____

_____

NAME_____ DATE_____

Prayer Need or Concern

Standing on Scriptures

Praise Reports / Testimonies

Notes_____

Photo

NAME_____ DATE_____

Prayer Need or Concern

Standing on Scriptures

Praise Reports / Testimonies

Notes_____

Photo

NAME_____ DATE_____

Prayer Need or Concern

Standing on Scriptures

_____   _____

_____   _____

_____   _____

_____   _____

_____   _____

_____   _____

_____   _____

Praise Reports / Testimonies

_____

_____

_____

_____

_____

Notes_____   **Photo**

_____

_____

_____

_____

_____

_____

_____

NAME_____ DATE_____

Prayer Need or Concern

**Standing on
Scriptures**

_____   _____
_____   _____
_____   _____
_____   _____
_____   _____
_____   _____
_____   _____
_____   _____

Praise Reports / Testimonies

_____
_____
_____
_____
_____

Notes_____   **Photo**

_____
_____
_____
_____
_____
_____
_____
_____
_____

NAME_____ DATE_____

Prayer Need or Concern

Standing on Scriptures

Praise Reports / Testimonies

Notes_____

Photo

NAME_____ DATE_____

Standing on Scriptures

Prayer Need or Concern

_____   _____
_____   _____
_____   _____
_____   _____
_____   _____
_____   _____
_____   _____
_____   _____

Praise Reports / Testimonies

_____
_____
_____
_____
_____

Notes_____   **Photo**

_____

_____

_____

_____

_____

_____

_____

_____

NAME_____ DATE_____

Prayer Need or Concern

Standing on Scriptures

_____   _____
_____   _____
_____   _____
_____   _____
_____   _____
_____   _____
_____   _____

Praise Reports / Testimonies

_____
_____
_____
_____
_____

Notes_____   **Photo**

_____
_____
_____
_____
_____
_____
_____

NAME_____ DATE_____

Prayer Need or Concern

Standing on Scriptures

Praise Reports / Testimonies

Notes_____

Photo

NAME_____ DATE_____

Prayer Need or Concern

Standing on Scriptures

_____   _____

_____   _____

_____   _____

_____   _____

_____   _____

_____   _____

Praise Reports / Testimonies

_____

_____

_____

_____

Notes_____

Photo

_____

_____

_____

_____

_____

_____

_____

NAME_____ DATE_____

Prayer Need or Concern

**Standing on
Scriptures**

_____   _____
_____   _____
_____   _____
_____   _____
_____   _____
_____   _____
_____   _____

Praise Reports / Testimonies

_____
_____
_____
_____
_____

Notes_____   **Photo**

_____
_____
_____
_____
_____
_____
_____
_____

NAME_____ DATE_____

Prayer Need or Concern

Standing on Scriptures

_____ _____

_____ _____

_____ _____

_____ _____

_____ _____

_____ _____

_____ _____

Praise Reports / Testimonies

_____

_____

_____

_____

_____

Notes_____ **Photo**

_____

_____

_____

_____

_____

_____

_____

_____

NAME_____ DATE_____

Prayer Need or Concern

Standing on Scriptures

_____   _____
_____   _____
_____   _____
_____   _____
_____   _____
_____   _____
_____   _____

Praise Reports / Testimonies

_____
_____
_____
_____
_____

Notes_____

Photo

_____
_____
_____
_____
_____
_____
_____

NAME_____ DATE_____

Prayer Need or Concern

**Standing on
Scriptures**

_____   _____
_____   _____
_____   _____
_____   _____
_____   _____
_____   _____
_____   _____
_____   _____

Praise Reports / Testimonies

_____
_____
_____
_____
_____

Notes_____   **Photo**

_____

_____

_____

_____

_____

_____

_____

NAME_____ DATE_____

Prayer Need or Concern

Standing on Scriptures

Praise Reports / Testimonies

Notes_____

Photo

NAME_____ DATE_____

Prayer Need or Concern

Standing on Scriptures

Praise Reports / Testimonies

Notes_____

Photo

NAME_____ DATE_____

Prayer Need or Concern

Standing on Scriptures

Praise Reports / Testimonies

Notes_____

Photo

NAME_____ DATE_____

Prayer Need or Concern

Standing on Scriptures

_____   _____
_____   _____
_____   _____
_____   _____
_____   _____
_____   _____
_____   _____

Praise Reports / Testimonies

_____
_____
_____
_____
_____

Notes_____

Photo

_____
_____
_____
_____
_____
_____
_____
_____

NAME_____ DATE_____

Prayer Need or Concern

Standing on Scriptures

Praise Reports / Testimonies

Notes_____

Photo

NAME_____ DATE_____

Prayer Need or Concern

Standing on Scriptures

_____   _____
_____   _____
_____   _____
_____   _____
_____   _____
_____   _____
_____   _____

Praise Reports / Testimonies

_____
_____
_____
_____
_____

Notes_____   **Photo**

_____
_____
_____
_____
_____
_____
_____
_____

NAME_____ DATE_____

Prayer Need or Concern

Standing on Scriptures

_____   _____
_____   _____
_____   _____
_____   _____
_____   _____
_____   _____
_____   _____

Praise Reports / Testimonies

_____
_____
_____
_____

Notes_____   **Photo**

_____
_____
_____
_____
_____
_____
_____
_____

NAME_____ DATE_____

Prayer Need or Concern

Standing on Scriptures

_____   _____
_____   _____
_____   _____
_____   _____
_____   _____
_____   _____
_____   _____

Praise Reports / Testimonies

_____
_____
_____
_____
_____

Notes_____

Photo

_____
_____
_____
_____
_____
_____
_____
_____

NAME_____ DATE_____

Prayer Need or Concern

**Standing on
Scriptures**

Praise Reports / Testimonies

Notes_____

Photo

NAME_____ DATE_____

Prayer Need or Concern	Standing on Scriptures
_____	_____
_____	_____
_____	_____
_____	_____
_____	_____
_____	_____
_____	_____

Praise Reports / Testimonies

_____

_____

_____

_____

_____

Notes_____ **Photo**

_____

_____

_____

_____

_____

_____

_____

NAME_____ DATE_____

Prayer Need or Concern

Standing on Scriptures

Praise Reports / Testimonies

Notes_____

Photo

NAME_____ DATE_____

Prayer Need or Concern

Standing on Scriptures

_____ _____
_____ _____
_____ _____
_____ _____
_____ _____
_____ _____
_____ _____

Praise Reports / Testimonies

_____
_____
_____
_____
_____

Notes_____ **Photo**

_____

_____

_____

_____

_____

_____

_____

NAME_____ DATE_____

Prayer Need or Concern

Standing on Scriptures

_____   _____
_____   _____
_____   _____
_____   _____
_____   _____
_____   _____
_____   _____

Praise Reports / Testimonies

_____
_____
_____
_____

Notes_____   **Photo**

_____
_____
_____
_____
_____
_____
_____

NAME_____ DATE_____

Prayer Need or Concern

Standing on Scriptures

_____ _____
_____ _____
_____ _____
_____ _____
_____ _____
_____ _____
_____ _____
_____ _____

Praise Reports / Testimonies

_____
_____
_____
_____
_____

Notes_____

Photo

_____
_____
_____
_____
_____
_____

NAME_____ DATE_____

Prayer Need or Concern

Standing on Scriptures

_____   _____
_____   _____
_____   _____
_____   _____
_____   _____
_____   _____
_____   _____
_____

Praise Reports / Testimonies

_____
_____
_____
_____
_____

Notes_____

Photo

_____
_____
_____
_____
_____
_____
_____
_____

NAME_____ DATE_____

Prayer Need or Concern

Standing on Scriptures

Praise Reports / Testimonies

Notes_____

Photo

NAME_____ DATE_____

Prayer Need or Concern

Standing on Scriptures

Praise Reports / Testimonies

Notes_____

Photo

NAME_____ DATE_____

Prayer Need or Concern

Standing on Scriptures

Praise Reports / Testimonies

Notes_____

Photo

NAME_____ DATE_____

Prayer Need or Concern

Standing on Scriptures

Praise Reports / Testimonies

Notes_____

Photo

NAME_____ DATE_____

Prayer Need or Concern

Standing on Scriptures

_____   _____
_____   _____
_____   _____
_____   _____
_____   _____
_____   _____
_____   _____

Praise Reports / Testimonies

_____
_____
_____
_____
_____

Notes_____

Photo

_____
_____
_____
_____
_____
_____
_____
_____

NAME_____ DATE_____

Prayer Need or Concern

Standing on Scriptures

Praise Reports / Testimonies

Notes_____

Photo

NAME_____ DATE_____

Prayer Need or Concern

Standing on Scriptures

_____   _____
_____   _____
_____   _____
_____   _____
_____   _____
_____   _____
_____   _____

Praise Reports / Testimonies

_____
_____
_____
_____
_____

Notes_____   **Photo**

_____
_____
_____
_____
_____
_____
_____

NAME_____ DATE_____

Prayer Need or Concern

Standing on Scriptures

Praise Reports / Testimonies

Notes_____

Photo

NAME_____ DATE_____

Prayer Need or Concern

Standing on Scriptures

Praise Reports / Testimonies

Notes_____

Photo

NAME_____ DATE_____

Prayer Need or Concern

Standing on Scriptures

_____   _____
_____   _____
_____   _____
_____   _____
_____   _____
_____   _____
_____   _____
_____   _____

Praise Reports / Testimonies

_____
_____
_____
_____
_____

Notes_____   **Photo**

_____
_____
_____
_____
_____
_____
_____
_____

NAME_____ DATE_____

Prayer Need or Concern

Standing on Scriptures

_____ _____
_____ _____
_____ _____
_____ _____
_____ _____
_____ _____
_____ _____
_____ _____

Praise Reports / Testimonies

_____
_____
_____
_____
_____

Notes_____

Photo

_____
_____
_____
_____
_____
_____
_____
_____

NAME_____ DATE_____

Prayer Need or Concern

Standing on Scriptures

Praise Reports / Testimonies

Notes

Photo

NAME_____ DATE_____

Prayer Need or Concern

Standing on Scriptures

_____ _____
_____ _____
_____ _____
_____ _____
_____ _____
_____ _____
_____ _____
_____ _____

Praise Reports / Testimonies

_____
_____
_____
_____
_____

Notes_____

Photo

_____
_____
_____
_____
_____
_____
_____
_____

NAME_____ DATE_____

Prayer Need or Concern

Standing on Scriptures

_____   _____
_____   _____
_____   _____
_____   _____
_____   _____
_____   _____
_____   _____
_____   _____

Praise Reports / Testimonies

_____
_____
_____
_____
_____

Notes_____   **Photo**

_____
_____
_____
_____
_____
_____
_____
_____

NAME_____ DATE_____

Prayer Need or Concern

Standing on Scriptures

Praise Reports / Testimonies

Notes_____

Photo

NAME_____ DATE_____

Prayer Need or Concern

Standing on Scriptures

_____ _____
_____ _____
_____ _____
_____ _____
_____ _____
_____ _____
_____ _____
_____

Praise Reports / Testimonies

_____
_____
_____
_____
_____

Notes_____

Photo

_____
_____
_____
_____
_____
_____
_____
_____

NAME_____ DATE_____

Prayer Need or Concern

Standing on Scriptures

Praise Reports / Testimonies

Notes_____

Photo

NAME_____ DATE_____

Prayer Need or Concern

Standing on Scriptures

_____   _____
_____   _____
_____   _____
_____   _____
_____   _____
_____   _____
_____   _____
_____   _____

Praise Reports / Testimonies

_____
_____
_____
_____
_____

Notes_____   ## Photo

_____

_____

_____

_____

_____

_____

_____

_____

NAME_____ DATE_____

Prayer Need or Concern

**Standing on
Scriptures**

_____   _____
_____   _____
_____   _____
_____   _____
_____   _____
_____   _____
_____   _____
_____   _____

Praise Reports / Testimonies

_____
_____
_____
_____
_____

Notes_____   **Photo**
_____
_____
_____
_____
_____
_____
_____

NAME_____ DATE_____

Prayer Need or Concern

Standing on Scriptures

_____   _____
_____   _____
_____   _____
_____   _____
_____   _____
_____   _____
_____   _____
_____   _____

Praise Reports / Testimonies

_____
_____
_____
_____

Notes

_____
_____
_____
_____
_____
_____
_____
_____
_____

Photo

NAME_____ DATE_____

Prayer Need or Concern

Standing on Scriptures

Praise Reports / Testimonies

Notes_____

Photo

NAME_____ DATE_____

Prayer Need or Concern

**Standing on
Scriptures**

Praise Reports / Testimonies

Notes

Photo

NAME_____ DATE_____

Prayer Need or Concern

Standing on Scriptures

Praise Reports / Testimonies

Notes_____

Photo

NAME_____ DATE_____

Prayer Need or Concern

Standing on Scriptures

Praise Reports / Testimonies

Notes_____

Photo

NAME_____ DATE_____

Prayer Need or Concern

Standing on Scriptures

Praise Reports / Testimonies

Notes_____

Photo

NAME_____ DATE_____

Prayer Need or Concern

Standing on Scriptures

_____   _____
_____   _____
_____   _____
_____   _____
_____   _____
_____   _____
_____   _____

Praise Reports / Testimonies

_____
_____
_____
_____

Notes_____

Photo

_____
_____
_____
_____
_____
_____
_____

NAME_____ DATE_____

Prayer Need or Concern

Standing on Scriptures

Praise Reports / Testimonies

Notes_____

Photo

NAME_____ DATE_____

Prayer Need or Concern

Standing on Scriptures

_____   _____
_____   _____
_____   _____
_____   _____
_____   _____
_____   _____
_____   _____

Praise Reports / Testimonies

_____
_____
_____
_____
_____

Notes_____   ## Photo

_____
_____
_____
_____
_____
_____
_____
_____

NAME_____ DATE_____

Prayer Need or Concern

Standing on Scriptures

Praise Reports / Testimonies

Notes_____

Photo

NAME_____ DATE_____

Prayer Need or Concern

Standing on Scriptures

_____   _____
_____   _____
_____   _____
_____   _____
_____   _____
_____   _____
_____   _____
_____   _____

Praise Reports / Testimonies

_____
_____
_____
_____
_____

Notes_____

Photo

_____
_____
_____
_____
_____
_____
_____
_____

NAME_____ DATE_____

Prayer Need or Concern

Standing on Scriptures

_____   _____

_____   _____

_____   _____

_____   _____

_____   _____

_____   _____

_____   _____

Praise Reports / Testimonies

_____

_____

_____

_____

_____

Notes_____   **Photo**

_____

_____

_____

_____

_____

_____

_____

NAME_____ DATE_____

Standing on Scriptures

Prayer Need or Concern

_____   _____
_____   _____
_____   _____
_____   _____
_____   _____
_____   _____
_____   _____

Praise Reports / Testimonies

_____
_____
_____
_____
_____

Notes_____   **Photo**

_____
_____
_____
_____
_____
_____
_____

NAME_____ DATE_____

Prayer Need or Concern

Standing on Scriptures

Praise Reports / Testimonies

Notes_____

Photo

NAME_____ DATE_____

Prayer Need or Concern

Standing on Scriptures

_____   _____
_____   _____
_____   _____
_____   _____
_____   _____
_____   _____
_____   _____
_____   _____

Praise Reports / Testimonies

_____
_____
_____
_____
_____

Notes_____   **Photo**

_____
_____
_____
_____
_____
_____
_____
_____

NAME_____ DATE_____

Prayer Need or Concern

Standing on Scriptures

Praise Reports / Testimonies

Notes_____

Photo

NAME_____ DATE_____

Prayer Need or Concern

Standing on Scriptures

_____   _____
_____   _____
_____   _____
_____   _____
_____   _____
_____   _____
_____   _____

Praise Reports / Testimonies

_____
_____
_____
_____
_____

Notes_____

Photo

_____
_____
_____
_____
_____
_____
_____
_____

NAME_____ DATE_____

Prayer Need or Concern

Standing on Scriptures

_____   _____
_____   _____
_____   _____
_____   _____
_____   _____
_____   _____
_____   _____
_____

Praise Reports / Testimonies

_____
_____
_____
_____
_____

Notes_____   **Photo**

_____
_____
_____
_____
_____
_____
_____
_____

NAME_____ DATE_____

Prayer Need or Concern

Standing on Scriptures

Praise Reports / Testimonies

Notes_____

Photo

NAME_____ DATE_____

Prayer Need or Concern

Standing on Scriptures

Praise Reports / Testimonies

Notes_____ **Photo**

NAME_____ DATE_____

Prayer Need or Concern

Standing on Scriptures

Praise Reports / Testimonies

Notes_____

Photo

NAME_____ DATE_____

Prayer Need or Concern

Standing on Scriptures

Praise Reports / Testimonies

Notes_____

Photo

NAME_____ DATE_____

Prayer Need or Concern

Standing on Scriptures

_____ _____
_____ _____
_____ _____
_____ _____
_____ _____
_____ _____
_____ _____

Praise Reports / Testimonies

_____
_____
_____
_____
_____

Notes_____

_____

_____

_____

_____

_____

_____

_____

Photo

NAME_____ DATE_____

Prayer Need or Concern

Standing on Scriptures

_____   _____
_____   _____
_____   _____
_____   _____
_____   _____
_____   _____
_____   _____

Praise Reports / Testimonies

_____
_____
_____
_____
_____

Notes_____   **Photo**

_____
_____
_____
_____
_____
_____
_____

NAME_____ DATE_____

Prayer Need or Concern

Standing on Scriptures

Praise Reports / Testimonies

Notes_____

Photo

NAME_____ DATE_____

Prayer Need or Concern

Standing on Scriptures

Praise Reports / Testimonies

Notes_____

Photo

Made in the USA
Las Vegas, NV
14 December 2021

37694903R00072